COMPLIMENTS OF YOUR VOLKSWAGEN DEALER

think small.

Charles Addams
Chon Day
Eldon Dedini
John Gallagher
Harry Golden
Lawrence Goodridge
Bob Grossman
William Hoest
Phil Interlandi
Anatol Kovarsky
Robert Kraus
Lee Lorenz
Charles E. Martin
Henry Martin
Joseph Mirachi
William O'Brian
Virgil Partch
George Price
Roger Price
Mischa Richter
Al Ross
Charles Saxon
Jean Shepherd
Claude Smith
H. Allen Smith
William Steig
James Stevenson
Barney Tobey
Bob Weber
Gahan Wilson
Joseph Zeis

What's So Funny About A Volkswagen?

by Herb Valen

A large man drove a small car into the lobby of a building in mid-town Manhattan. The doorman was annoyed. He was even more distressed when the man drove it onto the number one elevator, and pushed the UP button.

"You're supposed to use the service elevator" the doorman shouted up the elevator shaft, but The Man From Volkswagen wasn't listening. He had his mind on something else.

He drove into my studio and parked alongside my desk. I swiveled my chair around, and he stuck his head out the window of the car and looked me in the eye.

"You know what's the funniest car in the world?" he asked seriously.

"Is it made in Detroit?" I asked logically.

He shook his head, and pointed proudly to the car he was sitting in.

"Volkswagen?" I asked with uncertainty.

"Volkswagen!" he answered with certainty "Absolutely funniest car going. People cracking wise about Volkswagen everywhere you turn. And that's why I'm here. I want to get together the funniest cartoonists in the world, and the funniest writers in the world, and have them create a new, funny, marvelous Volkswagen book! All they've got to do is think small!"

"Think small," I said in a wee voice.

"All those big guys . . . Charles Addams, Charles Saxon, Virgil Partch, William Steig, George Price . . . Could you get them to think small, do you think?" he asked nervously.

"Infinitesimal," I said confidently.

"Jean Shepherd, Roger Price, Harry Golden, H. Allen Smith and all the other great ones? Could *they* think small?"

"Microscopic," I said in my largest voice.

"Okay!" And he put the car in gear, turned around on the rug, and buzzed out the door. "Small," he called over his shoulder as he whizzed into the elevator.

And so I got down to the hilarious task of getting together a funny book. And it turned out that the bigger the artist or writer, the smaller he could think, and one by one the funny funny drawings and pieces came across my desk, and the day dawned some months later when, lo and behold, there was a book.

Ah yes, *there* was a book! Laughed themselves sick they did. But we forgot one thing. When some thirty great cartoonists and writers start thinking — even thinking small — you end up with something BIG!

And here it is — something BIG about something small.

"You don't know what the thrill of the chase is, until you've ridden in one of these."

Eldon Dedini

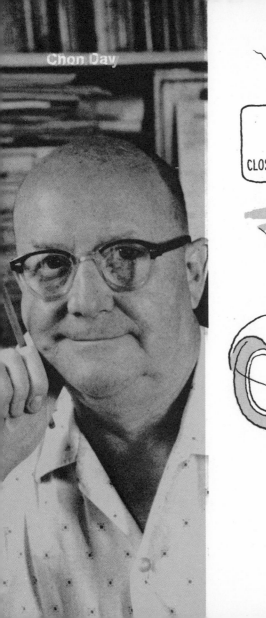

40%
GRADE
CLOSE GLOVE COMPARTMENT

"One thing's for sure. He's a member of the Coleoptera, but he's not a wood-boring beetle, a carpet-beetle, Japanese beetle, June beetle, snapping beetle, clicking beetle, water beetle . . ."

Robert Kraus

Anatol Kovarsky

"We'd better get out the rule book."

"Hand over your dough and a black raspberry popsicle."

Joseph Mirachi

"All main arteries are clear and traffic light and moving easily,
but I'll be delayed coming down because of a jam up here."

An Essay on the State of
the Internal Combustion Engine
Enthusiasts' Publications

or

Waiter, there's a Fly in my Magneto.

by Lawrence Goodridge

The car explosion has crowded our streets and highways to be sure.
And Victory gardens have given way to multi-level parking towers. But now even on the newsstands we find that travel mags, digests, family mags, model builders mags, girly mags, sports mags, anthologies and comic books about monsters we loved so well are being crowded aside by the steadily creeping proliferation of the genre known as the Car Lovers' Magazines—dedicated solely to the discussion and perpetuation of cars.

Generally they deal in two areas: (1) verbalizing the elusive aesthetics of yearly styling advances (you may laugh or cry) and (2) highly technical commentary on marvelous icons of our time such as double-barreled carburetors and solid valve lifters (the Italians are still enthralled with the Sistine Chapel). While these magazines vary in tone, all include a readers' column. Here the editors attempt to answer probing questions posed by leading thinkers from coast to coast. You know the kind.
J. J. S., from Umpa, Pa., writes:

Dear Sir:
I recently came across a 1924 Packard in-line 16 engine in virtually mint condition. What special difficulties might I encounter in adapting it for my 1949 Crosley?
Or S. R., from Sprockett, Ohio, who writes:

Dear Sir:
I have just installed a 500 cubic inch Golden Thruster engine in my 1951 schoolbus. Although low end torque has been improved, I am experiencing rear spring windup and excessive wheel hop at speeds over 85 mph. Also my gas mileage has suffered somewhat (3 mpg down to 2). Can you help me? The schoolboard is getting suspicious.

So the editor, who understands all this, his heart throbbing with remorse for S. R., for instance, prescribes instant panacea in similar prose—tells him to have his head torqued (or is it heads—somehow the former seems more apropos).

Thus I am left in total confusion by car magazines. What is rear spring windup? What is wheel hop? This pedantic jargon is blatant discrimination against the legions of sensitive, highly intelligent men and women who are indeed concerned about their cars, but in simple, less technical fashion. If my car doesn't run, being advised to have my conical frammis rebored is hardly enlightening.

Arise friends! What we need is our own magazine, called, conceivably, THE BEFUDDLED CAR OWNER'S GUIDE—for the man who doesn't even know what a oscilloscope is, much less own one. No obtuse slang. No gutsy descriptions. Just plain homespun talk about cars, and, praise be, a readers' column that doesn't require English subtitles. At last, J. B. from Boise, Idaho may write unashamedly:

Dear Sir:
A friend of mine recently recommended that I install a chrome heat riser in my car. What is a heat riser anyway? I've been so heartsick and confused over this, I've lost 75 pounds.

                                        Bewildered J. B.

Dear Bewildered J. B.:
Golly, everyone knows that hot air moves up and correspondingly, I think, a heat riser is an object that aids heat in rising so that your car doesn't tend to catch on fire as much. I think a chrome heat riser would be very nice.*

                                        Chin up,
*Especially with dark socks.   Ed.

And more serious problems—that elusive noise, for example. R. C. Y. writes:

Dear Sir:

Every time I hit the smallest bump there is an odd sound in the back of my car. It goes whunk-rrrbrbrbrbr-ka-chunk-slosh, followed by a faint ta-weeta-weeta. Am I in for an expensive repair job?

R. C. Y.

Dear R. C. Y.:

Nonsense. Simply open your trunk and remove that half-filled bottle of chianti that is rolling back and forth between your fender and tool kit. Next, very carefully inspect that pile of unsightly trash and rags behind your spare tire— you will find a nest of baby starlings that would probably be happier (and safer) in a nice quiet tree (NOTE: This may void your warranty.)

Ed.

Dear Sir:

On trips to my mother-in-law's home in Peoria, we use the flat open glove compartment door of our 1959 Volkswagen as a "traveler's dinette table." While detouring over a bumpy road recently, a pistachio milk shake overturned on my wife's wool plaid slacks. What should I do?

J. H. M.

Dear J. H. M.:

It just so happens that I know a very good dry cleaner on the corner of 48th and Spruce in Peoria. Tell him I sent you.

Ed.

But this marvelous pragmatism must ultimately be doomed to failure. Its purity cannot last. Soon, T. B. C. O. GUIDE would draw readers from all those "other magazines" and soon some day its charm would succumb to:

Dear Sir:

I have just installed a 500 cubic inch. . . . .

"Roy, shouldn't we have turned left at the beanstalk?"

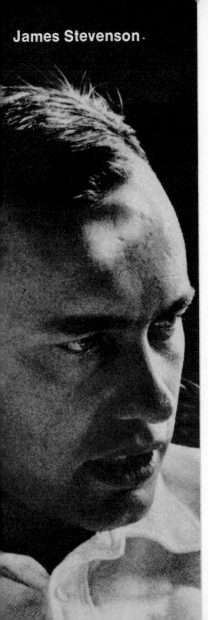

James Stevenson

"That's an extremely strong and dedicated group of law officers."

"And now the traffic report. The Lincoln and Holland tunnels are moderate to heavy, and extremely *heavy* traffic on the George Washington Bridge..."

"I understand he outgrew dashboard stereo."

"I'm worried about Lem. Here comes his Volks without him."

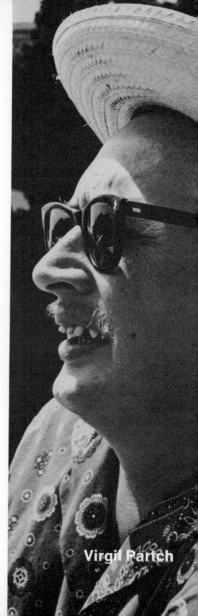

Virgil Partch

"Say! There's a lot of room under that hood!"

"Oh, oh! I'm afraid it's not going to turn out to be as old a civilization as we thought."

Mischa Richter

William Steig

"You can't drive and that's all there is to it!"

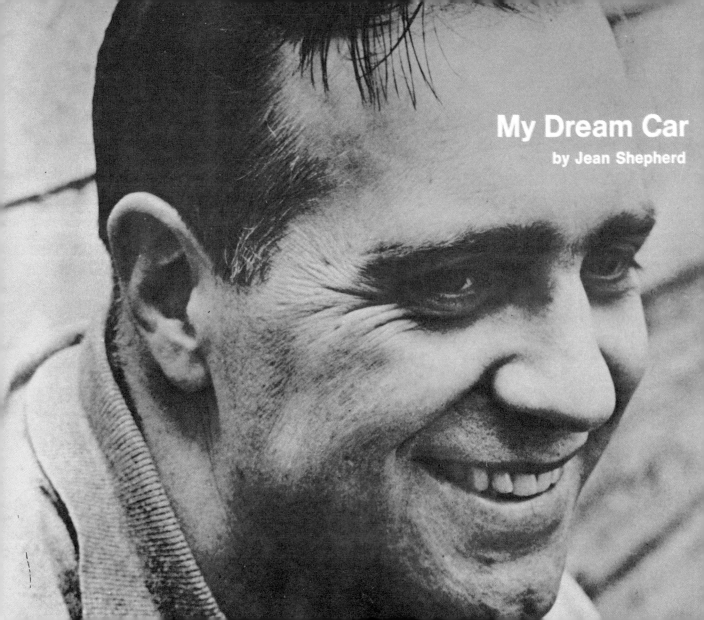

My Dream Car
by Jean Shepherd

The other night, as I lay safely sealed in the warm, comforting womb of my trundle bed, dozing fitfully after my long nightly bout of Late Late movies, the strains of Donald O'Connor's high, piping voice still ringing in the echoing caverns of my mind, an old, troublesome vision glowed faintly somewhere near the vicinity of the ceiling and then vanished. I sat up, beads of sweat instantly forming themselves on my pinched brow. I had seen that same vision many times over the years. It was an old enemy, and had caused me hours of soul-searching, and indeed perhaps accounts for my well-defined but nicely-hidden sense of deep inferiority. I had never spoken of this problem to others since, after all, there are some things best left lying quietly in the closets of the soul. But now I feel, since there could conceivably be others dogged by the same inadequacy, that in a spirit of Public Service it had all better come out.

It concerns that ubiquitous feature which runs over and over and over again in all Male-type magazines: My Dream Car. Hardly a Male periodical goes to press these days without a spectacularly illustrated piece by somebody named Ken something-or-other entitled "My Dream Car." It is as classical a piece of writing as a Hollywood western or a Broadway musical. It always follows the same well-worn paths and arrives at the same comfortable old destination. Its opening lines go like this:

I will never forget the day I stood by the side of that dusty country road, my hand comfortably held by the work-hardened mitt of my colorful grandfather Ebeneezer. There was a cloud of dust and a deep-throated, .heart-warming, thunderous boom as a great yellow speedster roared past, raising swirling clouds of dust and exhaust as it boomed over the hill. Crouched over the wheel, his oil-bespattered goggles glinting in the sun,

sat Dan Dangerfield, the local playboy and a student at that big college
up in the city, named Harvard.

Instantly my eyes glazed over as I fell madly and forever in love with
that belching monster. When the ground had ceased trembling under our
feet, old Grandpa cackled wheezily:

"Son, that's the greatest car Man ever built. That's the [Blank Blank]."
It was then I knew that some day I had to own a [Blank Blank].

The blanks are invariably filled with (1) Stutz Bearcat, (2) Mercedes 540
SK, (3) Mercer Raceabout, (4) Dusenberg SJ. The piece then invariably goes
on to tell of the author's harrowing thirty year search for the [Blank Blank]
and how, finally, tracking down an idle rumor heard in a barbershop, he
encounters in a broken-down old barn a [Blank Blank] owned by a
spectacularly folksy (1) Presbyterian minister, (2) crusty New England
farmer, or (3) eccentric collector of Yugoslavian coins, who then takes an instant
liking to the author and consents, after thirty years of loving care, to part
with this priceless family heirloom. The piece is always accompanied with
a magnificent four-color illustration of a classic [Blank Blank].

Now I don't take issue with this delicious bit of confection. I suppose,
in the end, it is as harmless as a Doris Day/James Garner romance, but it
has nevertheless left its scar on what remains of my self respect. It is difficult
to admit, even to your closest friends, that you have never had a love affair
with a Dusenberg or a Stutz Bearcat and, in fact, don't even remember
hearing of them, much less seeing one, in your mis-spent youth. Furthermore,
it is an even crummier feeling to *have* a dream car that you're even ashamed
to talk about. I might as well let it come out now, even though Ken
Whatever-his-name-is (it's something like Perky, or Puppy) would probably

not even wish to acknowledge my existence if he ever hears of this, which I doubt.

The truth of the matter is I'm not sure that my dream car even exists, or ever was. It is never in classic car shows. It is never mentioned in glossy volumes of great automobiles of the past. And on the few occasions that I have dared to bring it up, I get nothing but blank stares.

It all began when I was a pale-cheeked lad hurling newspapers into drainage gutters in a Northern Indiana mill town. Daily I would take a short cut through a shoddy, wind-blown Used Car lot where many a humbled used car buyer had been bilked of his life savings and then some. It was not exactly a Used Car lot; more of a defeated car graveyard. Elderly battered hulks, their original color and shape long since lost in the misty shades of the past rested in ragged rows, hubcap-deep in beer cans and cigar butts, awaiting hopefully one last owner. Overhead, a red and white sign banged in the wind: "HAPPY HARRY THE HUNGRY ARMENIAN   CARS BOUGHT AND SOLD   WE NEED CASH! LATE MODELS OUR SPECIALTY.   NO SIGNATURE NEEDED."

Occasionally Harry himself, his beady eyes glowing in the naked lightbulbs that hopefully lent a fictitious sheen to the hoods of his mortgaged clunkers, could be seen skulking about the premises, stuffing a wad of gum into a leaky radiator here, or dusting stove black over a cracked block there; always cheerful, always confident, ready for a deal.

Every night I hurried through Happy Harry's on my way to the next street, which lay at the end of my endless paper route. Gradually I began to know every battered hulk on Harry's lot. They would come and go. Some would remain longer than others. Some never went at all, and are probably still there, buried now in the mud, awaiting the archeologist's pick.

One dark, dreary day when the wind bore a cutting edge to it and even

Harry's lightbulbs looked discouraged, I first encountered the car which today
I doubt even existed. It was square and runty, a strangely mis-shapen, irritated
little car. Some machines are majestic; others voluptuous. A few are arrogant
and sleek. This car, if it was anything, radiated an aura of aggressive timidity.
Ironically, it bore proudly on the pocked and rusted hubcaps, in classic bas-relief,
the profile of a famous football coach, a football coach who was a demi-god
in the Midwest, a football coach whose very name was synonymous with
success and victory.

I had never seen such a car. My sack of sodden papers hanging heavy
on my shoulder, I circled this dun-colored, stunted little entry in the great
American automobile sweepstakes. Sure enough, on its tarnished radiator, in
bronze letters, was the name of the coach himself. The windshield bore in large,
runny whitewash lettering its price: eighteen dollars.

I circled it warily. Of course, I was far too young to own a car, but I looked
at them plenty and thought about them constantly. I peered in at its dim,
cramped little dashboard and stood back to get the whole picture. Harry,
sensing a nibble, was on the scene instantly, licking his chops.

"A beauty, ain't it, son?"

"Yep," I answered, "sure is."

"Just one owner."

"Yeah." I answered.

"Yep, Baptist Sunday School teacher. Old Lady. Just used it for picnics
on Sunday."

The cutting wind tinkled the bare lightbulbs overhead as we both gazed
approvingly at the little car which noticeably sagged in the middle.

"Yeah. You ask your Dad about her. He'll tell you." Harry was gone, back

into his little wooden shack to continue his endless game of Deuces Wild
solitaire. I scurried over the rest of my route, thinking about the car that I did
not realize at the time would become a secret, ghostly mirage in my later life.

That night at the supper table, in the warm air of our kitchen, an atmosphere
heavy with the aroma of red cabbage and meatloaf, I put it to the Old Man.
He was a recognized local expert on the folklore and mythology of the Used Car,
a walking compendium of the intricate knowledge of a highly complex field
of study. He knew intimately the vintage years, the years of drought of all the
various breeds of machines that roamed the back alleys of the Midwest.

"Dad . . ." I began. He laid down the Sport page and prepared to dispense
advice and knowledge.

"Dad, Happy Harry has got a funny car on his lot that I never heard of."

"Yeah? What is it?" Such a statement always brought the Old Man's
mind to full attention. There were two subjects that involved his entire life;
Used Cars and the White Sox, an obscure ball team of the Chicago area.

"Well, it's got this guy's picture on the hubcaps."

"What guy?"

"That football coach." I couldn't remember his name.

"Football coach? You mean Happy Harry the hungry Armenian has got
on his lot a *Rockne?*"

His voice rose in obvious interest.

"Yeah, that's it, a Rockne."

"Well, I'll be damned. A Rockne. How much does he want for it?"

"Eighteen dollars." I answered.

"That crook!" The Old Man laughed appreciatively. He and Harry were
old adversaries.

"I never heard of a Rockne." I continued gamely, hoping he would say something nice about it.

"Son, the Rockne is the second-worst piece of junk ever made! Next to the Essex Super 6. It's got a transmission made out of balsa wood. The only time I ever saw a Rockne do over 25 on the flat was the time I saw one get smacked in the rear by a Western Avenue streetcar going full tilt, and then the guy couldn't get it stopped for two blocks because it didn't have any brakes. Eighteen bucks for a Rockne! Well, you gotta hand it to old Harry for trying."

The next day I could hardly wait to get back to the end of my route so I could see the Rockne again. I hurried through the rows of dilapidated heaps to the spot where it stood. It was gone. In its place an old Hudson convertible sat rusting away quietly. I never again saw another Rockne.

Or heard of them, for that matter. And now, at this long last, I have begun to doubt whether they really existed. Did I make up this scene? Was there ever a Rockne? I find it hard to believe that the great giant of the Fighting Irish would have lent his name to such a loser. I have never been able to shake that vague, insistent desire to see one, to sit in one, maybe even to own one. I know it is shameful to admit that my dream car did not thunder, sending up great, billowing clouds of dust as it roared over the brick oval at Indianapolis. Some men dream big. Others dream little. I hope Ken Whatshisname won't think too evil of me for this abject admission. But there it is. A man sometimes has to face himself and admit what he is. Sometimes I awake in the dark in the early morning hours and imagine that I see a scuttling, dun-colored Rockne limping around a corner and struggling into a service station. And then my dream fades, leaving only the sighing wind. Was there ever a Rockne? Or have I dreamed it all?

Joseph Zeis

"They certainly make those Volks' airtight."

1.

2.

3.

4.

5.

Phil Interlandi

"It's given him an inferiority complex. Now he hardly ever mentions going seven days without water."

Gahan Wilson

Claude Smith

"Keep walking. Pretend he doesn't belong to us."

Rearrangements: from the Winton to the Volkswagen.

by Harry Golden

I am 63, but I remember the first automobile I saw and touched. It was, as I recall, when I was eight years old and lived on the Lower East Side of New York, a ghetto enclave filled with teeming tenements. A son of one of our neighbors was a chauffeur. He wore a light blue uniform with black boots he strapped together. He was always carrying big, heavy bear rugs with which to cover the feet of his employer. He drove for an uptown doctor. Now and then the young chauffeur would drive down from the fancy neighborhood for lunch and park in front of the next-door tenement. We kids stood around staring at the car a long time, waiting for this young chauffeur to come out and watch him start it up again.

Once he appeared we threw a barrage of questions at him, imploring answers, pleading for a chance to touch the car, investigate it, ride in it maybe. On several occasions, he lifted the hood for us to see what was inside. He was afraid to give us a ride, afraid his boss would spot dirt we probably would track in. But it was enough to see that auto, touch it, and walk around it. I've never forgotten that car. Its name was Winton.

From that Winton in 1910 to the Volkswagen of today is a history of a time which saw us go from a small town rural civilization to a huge urban complex, the most mobile society in world history. America is on wheels. The car has rearranged our lives and changed our habits. The poet Carl Sandburg saw this coming 40 years ago when he wrote:

It's a lean car . . . a long-legged dog of a car . . . a gray-ghost
   eagle car.
The feet of it eat the dirt of a road . . . the wings of it
   eat the hills.
Danny the driver dreams of it when he sees women in red skirts
   and red sox in his sleep.
It is in Danny's life and runs in the blood of him . . . a lean
   gray-ghost car.
Sandburg not only foresaw the tremendous mobility of the

American culture but also the place the automobile would have in the minds of the millions of American Dannys who would see women in "red skirts and red socks" in dreams.

It is hardly a coincidence that most of our Dannys today refer to their cars as "she," polish "her" night and day, tear "her" apart and hope to put "her" back together again. The car never cloys his appetite. Like Cleopatra herself she indeed "makes hungry where most she satisfies." She is always new, new every year.

Let's face it—the automobile has an utter fascination for the American male, for the male everywhere in the world. He can make and remake, buy and rebuy that car endlessly. Millions of young fellows think nothing of using the frame of one old car, the engine of another, the body parts of yet a third, and different elements like transmissions and wheels and hubcaps from still more to fashion their own models. Arab potentates in the near-East order the first fifty Cadillacs off the assembly line year after year, never uncrating some of them. The car is an ego idea which can be worried over endlessly, adorned and readorned, adjusted, readjusted, toyed with, played with, manipulated, redone, sometimes simply owned until finally traded off or sold so that the process begins all over again. The car has rearranged our life because it has become part of it, not as a possession but as an idea, an extension of life, as the hearth became an extension of civilized man.

I certainly do not mean to over-emphasize the physiological symbolism of the car. That is only one of its aspects. The major function of the car, social transportation, means for the first time people can travel without a specific destination. They simply pack their tensions, their frustrations and unfulfilled yearnings into the automobile and they're off. "Going for a drive" they call it.

Travel was once the most difficult of a man's preoccupations—now it is one of the easiest. When one of my neighbors returned after an absence of three weeks, I asked him where he'd been.

"Took the wife and three kids and her mother out to the Grand Canyon,"
he said.

"What airline did you fly?" I asked.

"No airline," he replied. "Used the Volkswagen. Camped in state parks
all the way."

"Wasn't it uncomfortable?" I pursued, meaning wasn't it crowded.

"Up to the Carlsbad Caverns it was bad but then I told the old battle-axe
if she didn't stop the backseat driving, I'd park her with the other daughter in
Minneapolis. Didn't have a bit of trouble the rest of the way out or back."

This situation reminds me of the old-time cobblers who didn't make a boot
for the left foot and another for the right, but used the same last for both. It
became a question then not whether the shoe fit but whether the foot would
fit the shoe. And the car is so much an extension of our lives we no longer worry
will it accommodate us, but will we accommodate it.

Thus constructive leisure to millions of working men is not the
self-improvement of opera or literature nor the physical abandon of fishing or
gardening, but the thrill of driving to the job in a new car. Nor do I despair that
this is so. Certainly a new car is indicative of complex needs in complex times
in complex places. The car provides personal, individual mobility on a vast scale.
It is the car which makes the city obsolete as a place of habitation, which is
perhaps why we treat our cities so badly.

Just how complex I never realized until I owned my first car back in 1923.
Or let's say, I was a partner in the title to a 1921 Essex with three others. Three
of my friends and I each chipped in $40. Eventually each of us qualified for a
driver's license by which time, of course, the Essex needed a new battery since
the old one was dormant for so long. But our troubles were just beginning.

"Who has the car?" George would ask.

"Murray must have it," I answered. So John and I took the long subway
ride to the outer reaches of the Bronx, scouted up Murray only to hear he was
sure George had picked it up the night before. Down to Columbia University,

waiting outside Hamilton Hall until George exited from a class, then to learn, "No, I don't have it. I haven't seen it since Tuesday."

"Well, who's got the car?"

My own brother, Max, had the car.

"Max," I said, "it's one thing to steal my socks and wear them to play basketball until they stand up by themselves. It's another thing, a serious thing, to borrow a car in which I only have a one-fourth interest."

"Now Harry," Max answered, "how did you expect me to get from Stuyvesant High School on Fourteenth Street to Evander Childs High School in the Bronx? With all the basketball equipment?"

We issued schedules as detailed and as solemn as a White Paper, and no sooner were they issued than abrogated. There was always a good reason why you had to surrender your turn and always a better reason why you had to usurp someone else's. And our difficulties in apportioning that cost of gasoline was a fractional problem the new math couldn't solve.

The four-family car has given way to the two-car family, but the contention, I believe, is still with us. So is the problem of who's to fill the gas tank. It is still unresolved. But no complaints. Not from me. I'm merely emphasizing the fact that the car has become the symbol of our very lives and hopes for the future. It certainly is the symbol of our entire economy and well-being. For seventy-five years of the industrial revolution, the stock market waited breathlessly every week for the number of "carloadings"—the measure of our economic health. Today and for the last twenty-five years automotive production is the gauge.

How many millions of families earn their living from automotive production and all its allied industries and subsidiaries I will leave to others. I know the car represents the major portion of our productivity and industrial growth, whether this, all of it, is good or bad—let us wait and see. But as a member of this society, understanding what makes it go, I salute the auto men, from the big Cadillacs down to the modest Volkswagen. We hope and pray for their continued success.

Lee Lorenz

"By George! It's good to see someone who's kept faith with the American dream."

"Need a fourth, lady? I play bridge."

Al Ross

Henry Martin

"Which way to the Autobahn, old woman?"

"A fine time to be coming home. I put you in the driver's seat, and I can take you out of the driver's seat!"

Charles Saxon

"Professor Enright, remember me? Dickie Atwell. You flunked me in Business Administration."

The Sad Story of the Manufacturer, the High Powered Adman and the Motivational Expert.

by Roger Price

An Automobile Manufacturer once paid an unexpected call on a High Powered Adman. "We're thinking of switching agencies," he said.

The Adman's adrenal glands stirred sluggishly. He nodded.

"Our car, the Bobbit-8, as you may know, is not one of the Big Three. But now it's even dropped out of the Big Thirty. We sold fourteen last year—fourteen—all to members of the firm. And those," he moaned, "were sold at employee discount."

"That's not good enough," said the Adman, going right to the heart of the problem as was his wont. "There has to be a reason why Joe Blow isn't line-wise making a bee for the Bobbit-8. Question: Is the car any good?"

"What's to be good?" said the Manufacturer. "It's just a standard car-type car. It costs four grand, it has a 500 horse power engine, adjusto-reclining seats, wall-to-wall carpet and it falls apart in 22 months."

"What has been your pitch, ad-wise?"

"The Bumble, Stumble and Fall crowd came up with this real catchy slogan: The Bobbit-8 is Real Fine. (But then, BS & F made their reputation on understatement.) We print it on cocktail napkins and give them away at PTA meetings."

The Adman nodded and put his fingertips together. "Just off the top of my head, I'll throw this in the pot for free," he said. "I feel that slogan might be improved. Ummm." He tilted back in his executive chair and frowned. Small sparks flew from his ears. "How about . . ." he said slowly, "How about . . . if it was 'The Bobbit-8 is *Great!*' Seems to have more pizazz that way."

"By God," said the Manufacturer, intending no blasphemy, but merely expressing the depth of his emotion. "By God, it even rhymes. That is real *creativity!*"

"The name of the game," said the Adman.

"The BS & F bunch spent 3 months brainstorming their slogan, and you've out-creativitied them in less than a minute," said the Manufacturer, visibly impressed. "I am visibly impressed and am switching agencies pronto."

He immediately wrote a most sizable check for and tossed it on the desk. "You now have the Bobbit account," he said.

They both stood up and thrust out their hands. "Welcome aboard," they said in unison.

It was seven weeks to the day when the High Powered Adman next summoned the Bobbit-8's president. The meeting place was again the agency's plush conference room. "We've got the pitch," he announced. "It's Youth."

"Youth?" inquired the Manufacturer nervously. "You mean those Zootsuiters?"

"No, no," said the Adman. "Youth today is a concept. America thinks Young. They want youthful symbols. We'll give the Bobbit-8 a new Image that will be in the groove with all the hep-cats and register solid, Jackson, with the rug cutters."

"Say, you sure understand their lingo," said the Manufacturer. "But how are we gonna do all this?"

"We'll call in a Motivational Expert," said the Adman. He reached forward and pushed a button.

At once a bilious cloud of yellow smoke appeared in the center of the office. From within could be heard the sound of violent coughing.

In a moment the smoke disappeared into the air conditioning vent, revealing the Motivational Expert. Adjusting his conical hat, he drew a pentagram on the floor and scattered a bit of Powdered Bat here and there.

"American men," he intoned, "are afraid of their women. They need to express their unexpressed feeling of suppressed masculinity. To them, Youth means Masculinity and Freedom. Freedom means Irresponsibility. Their idea of Youth is a 17-year-old punk wearing a leather jacket, who is found irresistible by 16-year-old blondes."

"What about women buyers?" said the Adman.

"The appeal is the same. The women also want to be Young, Masculine and Free. Their idea of Youth is a 16-year-old blonde sitting between the bucket seats of a custom job with two 17-year-old punks wearing leather jackets." He paused to scatter some more Bat on the Pentagram. "Here's an idea. Let's toss it into the cauldron and see if it bubbles. First, we give the Bobbit a new name, which will *say* Youth! A name like The Assassin, The Mugger, The Piranha, The Black Widow . . ."

"How about The Maniac, The Schizoid, The Psychedelic?" said the Adman, his eyes gleaming.

The M.E. shook his head, "Get the shop working on it," he said. "In the meantime, for sales potential, the car must be redesigned to substantiate the Youthful Image."

"Why not?" said the Manufacturer.

"Here are new specifications," said the M.E. Then, with a sweep of his velour cape, he disappeared in a fresh bilious yellow cloud, leaving behind a slight smell of brimstone and martinis.

The following year the new, new, new Bobbit was the hit of the Auto Show. Only it was now called "The Cutthroat." Commercials and display ads proclaimed it: *The Young Youth Car of the Year— For Cool, In, Hip, Swinging Swingers Only!"*

The Cutthroat had a nylon-fringed top which hung down over the sides like a Beatle cut. It had black leather tires, Mary Quant upholstery, a Pop-Mod color scheme (green, purple and red) and Hip-Hugger safety belts. Instead of a steering wheel it had motorcycle handlebars. Standard equipment included a 12-speed stereo record player, a coke and snack bar, Bell-bottom Fenders and Mini-Bumpers. And with each car, the dealers gave away a dozen sweat shirts with the sleeves torn out.

Youthful, swinging Americans of all ages (except those under 25) stormed the Bobbit showrooms demanding The Cutthroat. It was a smash.

But, alas, it didn't last. Due to a fatal miscalculation, each and every Bobbit Cutthroat had to be recalled.

Four weeks after leaving the factory—all of them developed acne.

FALLEN
ROCK
ZONE

"You got in. You get out!"

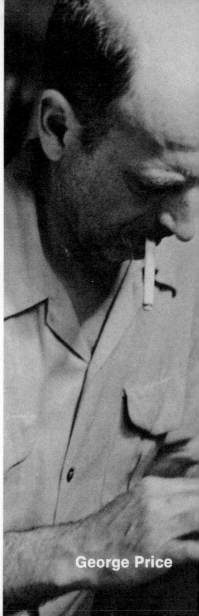

George Price

"He's the one luxury we allow ourselves."

"Our kids have things a lot easier than we ever had them. He used to drive a Rolls."

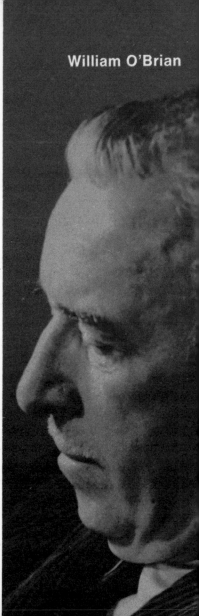

William O'Brian

Charles E. Martin

Far-Out Drivers I Have Known

by H. Allen Smith

*Author's Note: When VW asked me to write a story for a joke book they
were publishing, I had to confess that all I knew about Volkswagen was the
relative advantage of their 4-passenger convertible over their bus.*

*My daughter has four young sons, wilder than the wildest Comanches.
Her husband bought a Volkswagen bus for her to use in hauling them from here
to there and back to here. Each of her four boys has a friend or two, and
often some of these friends would come along for the ride, and some of them
had dogs, and the dogs enjoyed shunpike tours. My daughter finally set up
a holler. "This bus," she said, "has become a combination football field,
basketball court, boy scout camp and zoo." She solved her problem neatly;
turned in the bus and got a Volkswagen convertible bug. Four boys, maybe
one dog, sometimes one friend, plus my daughter as driver . . . and there is
no space for Comanche shennanigans.*

Let us proceed.

The late Fred Allen never learned to drive. He said there was no room for
such foolishness in his life, but I knew him quite well, and it is my conviction
that he was a-scairt of anything with a motor in it. Once when I was working
in Hollywood he came out to make a picture at Paramount. There was a scene
in the picture wherein he was supposed to emerge from a restaurant, get
into a big car and drive away. He had to move a mere thirty feet — just far enough
to get out of camera. After some minimal directions, they tried him on
the set, where he came close to slaughtering a motley assortment of grips,
dinkies, actors, juicers, button-dusters and associate producers. Clearly
he needed additional instruction.

A guy took him to the desert where he couldn't hit anything but cactus and worked with him for two days. Fred flunked door-opening, couldn't find the starter button, and broke out in a sweat when he was told to put his hand on the gearshift lever. He cussed some, too.

So how did they work it? They hooked wires onto the car; he came out of the restaurant and got into the driver's seat, with ample aplomb and authority; then he waggled the gearshift lever meaningfully and a tractor pulled the car out of camera range.

I once knew a mildly irascible man who was manager of a New York theater just a couple of blocks from the building where car-shy Fred Allen lived. Every afternoon around five this man's wife arrived and drove him home to Central Park West. He was always frightened by her driving, which he considered to be slipshod, unlawful, and clumsy. He often spoke harshly to her, saying he fully expected to die at her hands, any day. Yet for some reason she went merrily along unmangled, day after day and year after year. She never got tickets, she never had accidents, cops never chewed her out. This aggravated her husband almost beyond all endurance.

Then came The Day. She had picked him up and was driving up Sixth Avenue. At Central Park South she stopped until the cop at the intersection gave the go-signal. She moved forward and swung into the left turn. Midway in the turn a whistle sounded. Her husband looked back and saw the cop waving at *them*. "Now you've done it!" he said to his beloved. "I knew your damn-fool driving would get you in trouble!" He was burbling with inner joy and exultation. He could tell by the look on the approaching cop's face that she was finally gonna get it — a tongue-lashing at the very least, and maybe even a ticket.

He just sat with a slight smirk, smug in the knowledge that he lived in
a well-ordered world.

     The cop arrived and spoke forthrightly to the wife. "Lady," he said,
"I want to have a good close look at you. I have been standing on this corner three
years, three hideous years, the worst years of my life, and you are the first
person I ever seen who made this left turn the way God meant it oughta be made.
Lady, if I had a medal on me, I'd give it to you." With which he stepped
back, executed a low bow, and waved her on her way. My friend the theater
manager slid lower in his seat, grinding his teeth. He muttered something
about corny cops, under the heel of Tammany. And he quit speaking to his
treacherous helpmeet for three long days.

     Next let us consider my own wife. When I moved to the country quite a long
time ago, she had never driven a car (or even a nail). It was now obvious
that she had to learn. I didn't know that there is a basic rule in modern
civilization: No husband should ever attempt to teach his wife how to drive, unless
his aim is to lay down grounds for a divorce. I took her out twice. What I said
to her was, "X%#&Z!@X¢!!?+X!!!" over and over. For some reason she
resented this type of conversation, so she fired me as her instructor and sought
assistance at the garage where we did business. The owner of the place
took her out to a flat meadow and spent an hour with her. He told her that the
best way to teach a woman to drive is to have her drive backward. In reverse.
All the time. Anybody, he said, who can drive expertly in reverse can surely drive
expertly in the other direction. He brought her home and told her to practice
on our driveway (which was long as a city block and steep as the Matterhorn)
for a few days before venturing onto the public highways.

What followed was one of the most harrowing weeks of my life. Backward was the only way she wanted to drive. She had to go forward at times in order to get into position to go backward, but she was genuinely frightened of obstacles lying ahead of her. She backed into our rock garden. She backed into trees. She bashed in the front of my tool shed. She got the car hung up on a stone wall and the garage people had to come and derrick it off. They didn't make any critical remarks, but I noticed them shaking their heads in dismay.

Our son came home from engineering school and I assigned him the job of giving her driving lessons. He went out with her for two days and then came to me and said, "Dad, I can't take this. I'm beginning to forget that she's my mother."

I wanted to abandon the whole project, but she wouldn't, and I couldn't. I wanted desperately for her to learn to drive so she could go to town and buy the groceries and the chinchilla stoles and refills for my ballpoints.

Then on a Sunday afternoon the matter was resolved. The garage owner who advocated backward-driving came to my house with a friend. The friend turned out to be one of the most famous automobile drivers in the history of the carburetor. Ralph DePalma. Anyone of my generation will remember him—he was the Ty Cobb, the Jack Dempsey, the Pudge Heffelfinger of automobile racing. We sat on the terrace for a while and talked of the Indianapolis 500 and other internal combustion topics, and then a thought crossed my mind.

"Mr. DePalma," I said, "my wife here has been trying to learn to drive and she's having a little trouble. I wonder if you might be willing to take her out and give her a few pointers."

"Be happy to," he said, and off they went. They were gone a couple of hours and when they came back my wife was driving her car—frontward. She turned it around, almost expertly. The next day she drove alone to the village and got back alive and undented.

I have never quite trusted her. When it is necessary for me to ride with her, which isn't often, I sit in a crouch with one hand on the door handle, so I can make an emergency escape. I complain continually—she scooches the driver's seat up too close to the steering wheel; she doesn't sound her horn at dangerous curves; she doesn't angle correctly getting into the garage. But she only smiles and rolls bravely on her way, content in the knowledge that she's never had an accident, never been given a ticket. Her only response to my . . . well, my nagging, is to say, "You forget that I studied under Ralph DePalma."

It would only seem fair to me to bring myself into this gallery of drivers. I am one of those rare motorists who exercise caution far beyond the demands-of-duty whenever he is at the wheel. I give the business of driving my steady, alert, undivided attention at all times. I never take my eyes off the road except for brief scannings of hidden driveways and fallen rock zones. I carry a trunkful of emergency equipment—ropes, flares, first aid kits, hunting knives, two ropes, claw hammers, K-rations, wading boots and a bottle of No-Doz.

In short, folks, I'm a drivin' man. Just give me time to get muh revs reckoned, jiggle muh gear ratios a trifle, file down muh intake manifold and saturate muh sump, and . . . Zshwoooooooooooooosh! I'm ready for Clermont-Ferrand and the French Grand Prix. Driving what? Muh daughter's VW bug, fully equipped with all my gear plus four kids and a dog.

"Honey, could you help me get the car out of the garage?"

William Hoest

"Say . . . isn't that where we left off yesterday?"

"It should be a scintillating conversation. I'm placing a VW between a
Cadillac and a Lincoln Continental."

Bob Weber

"What did _you_ get?"

"I just had an idea. Why don't we make a beetle-shaped car that we
don't have to change the design of, year in and year out."

John Gallagher

"*I know how proud you are of the wagon, but I do wish you'd stop saying 'There's always room for one more.'*"

"Can we order one with bat fins?"